Gabrielle The Great

Tries Out!

Gabrielle the Great Tries Out! Gabrielle woke up every morning thinking she was pretty great. She sat up in her bed and whispered good morning to the trees and birds and clouds in the sky, poised as a young princess. She gazed around her room smiling at the art decor made by her own hands that adorned her walls. She closed her eyes and whispered a morning prayer, thanking the Creator for another day!

Gabrielle waited patiently for her father to come into her room and greet her as he always did: Good Morning Gabrielle the Great!! He would say, with a smile as long as the Mississippi River! He reminded her every day that she was great...just because she was Gabby.

Daddy lifted her up and carried her to the rest room where she prepared for the greatness of the day.

She washed her face hands and body, brushed her teeth and combed her hair.
She looked in the mirror, smiled, and said,

Gabby, you sure are great!

She climbed into her wheelchair and was ready to start the day.

Gabby was excited because her 4th grade class was preparing for the spring musical! Gabby absolutely loved to sing and dance! She had secretly decided to try out for one of the leading roles when the sign-up sheet for auditions was posted.

Gabby wanted to play the character of Charlotte in the musical Charlotte's web. She had read the story over and over, watched the movie, and come up with a unique way to play Charlotte. I hope I can sign up today, she thought!

When Gabby descended from the school bus, her friends and adult helper were there waiting.

She kept her secret safe in her heart and did not tell them about her intention to audition for the play.

Miss Carrie, Gabby's helper, wheeled her into the lunch room for breakfast.

Gabby sat with a group of her friends and laughed and ate. In Walked Mrs. Red, the music teacher, and posted the sign-up sheet for the play!

Gabby waited until breakfast was over and all the other students had signed their names.

She then asked Miss Carrie to wheel her over to the sign up sheet. Miss Carrie had a surprised smile on her face. Gabby wrote her name and went to class.

Later in the day an announcement came over the microphone throughout the school Asking everyone who had signed up for the musical to please report to the school gymnasium. It was time for tryouts!! Gabby and Miss Carrie hurried down the hall.

Several children were in the gym and appeared surprised to see Gabrielle. Some of the kids said really mean things to Gabby.

They laughed at her because she was in a wheelchair. Gabby remembered what her father told her: I'm great, just because I'm Gabby! She smiled inside and out and ignored the mean kids.

When it was her turn, Gabby read her lines loudly with a smile on her face. She added her special touch that she had been practicing.

The kids who were being mean stopped laughing and listened to Gabby.

When she was finished some of them even said she did a good job.

Gabby went back to class and was proud of herself for trying out. Later that day, Gabby found out that she got the part!

She felt good about herself because she tried her best and did not let the mean kids bother her.

She remembered the words of her father and she was a winner; not because she got the part, but because she did not give up.

I am Gabrielle the Great!

The End

This book is dedicated to my very own Gabby...Trinity Gabrielle

I named you Trinity because the number three stands for that which is solid, substantial, complete, and entire. All things that are special and complete are stamped with the number three. In the scriptures this completion becomes Divine so Trinity is symbolic of Divine perfection. Daughter, you are complete in the life of your mother and family. You were divinely created and despite your early arrival, I know that you have everything that you need to survive and complete your purpose in life.

Your middle name, Gabrielle, is the effeminate of Gabriel. Gabriel is an angel of heaven who appears to interpret visions, announce the birth of John the Baptist, and announce the birth of Jesus. I know that the message you have to bring to the world is a great one! You will do wonderful things and I can't wait to cheer you on.

I hope that the adventures of Gabby the Great inspire other children, both those who are developing typically and those who are differently abled, to be the BEST that they can be!

Love,

Mom

About Gabby's condition: Cerebral Palsy

Have you ever heard someone in your family talk about your first step or the first word you spoke? For kids with Cerebral Palsy, called CP for short, taking a first step or saying a first word is not so easy. That is because CP is a condition that can affect the things that kids do every day.

What is CP?

Some kids with CP use wheelchairs and others walk with the help of crutches or braces.In some cases, a kid's speech may be affected or the person might not be able to speak at all. Cerebral palsy (say: she-REE-brel PAWL-zee) is a condition that affects thousands of babies and children each year. It is not contagious which means you can't "catch" it from anyone who has it. The word cerebral means having to do with the brain. The word palsy means weakness or problem in the way a person moves or positions his/her body.

A kid with CP has trouble controlling the muscles of their body. Normally, the brain tells the rest of the body exactly what to do and when to do it. The brain is the BOSS! But because CP affects the brain, depending on what part of the brain is affected, a kid may not be able to walk, talk, eat, or play the way most kids do.

Types of CP

There are three types of cerebral palsy: spastic (say: SPASS-tik), athetoid (say:ATH-uh-toid), and ataxic (say: ay-TAK-sic). The most common type of CP is spastic. A kid with spastic AP can't relax his or her muscles so the muscles may be stiff. Athetoid CP affects a kid's ability to control the muscles. This means that the arms or legs that are affected my flutter or move suddenly. A kid with ataxic CP has problems with balance and coordination.

A kid with CP can have a mild case or a more severe case - it really depends on how much of the brain is affected and which parts of the body that section of the brain controls. If both arms and both legs are affected, a kid might need to use a wheelchair.

CEREBRAL PALSY:
The Six 'F-Words' For CP

1

FUNCTION I might do things differently but I CAN do them. How I do it is not important. Please let me try!

2  **FAMILY** They know me best and I trust them to do what's best for me. Listen to them. Talk to them. Hear them. Respect them.

3

FITNESS Everyone needs to stay fit and healthy, including me. Help me find ways to keep fit.

4  **FRIENDS** Having childhood friends is important. Please give me opportunities to make friends with my peers.

5

FUN Childhood is about fun and play. This is how I learn and grow. Please help me do the activities that I find the most fun.

6  **FUTURE** I will grow up one day, so please find ways for me to develop independence and be included in my community.

World Cerebral Palsy Day
worldcpday.org

Proudly supported by The Allergan Foundation

Based on Rosenbaum, P. & Gorter, J.W (2012), The 'F-words' in childhood disability: I swear this is how we should think! Child: Care, Health and Development, (38) 4. Visit https://www.canchild.ca/en/research-in-practice/f-words-in-childhood-disability for more resources.

www.canchild.ca

WORLD CEREBRAL PALSY DAY
05.OCT.2016

Discussion questions:

1. Do you know anyone who is different because they are in a wheelchair?

_____

2. What do you think about this person?

_____

3. Do you think that sometimes they feel like Gabby and get teased?

_____

4. Think of things that you have in COMMON with Gabby.
Write those in a list.

_____

5. What positive character traits can you show to a person who is in a wheelchair?

_____

Made in the USA
Monee, IL
26 August 2019